D1020255

GAELIC GHOSTS

GAELIC

GHOSTS

by Sorche Nic Leodhas

Illustrated by Nonny Hogrogian

Holt, Rinehart and Winston

New York · Chicago · San Francisco

3 ṭ|
10-22-64
398
al 35 q
c

To Michael McFarland Digby

By the Same Author

HEATHER AND BROOM / Tales of the Scottish Highlands
THISTLE AND THYME / Tales and Legends from Scotland
ALL IN THE MORNING EARLY

INTRODUCTION

IT HAS ALWAYS BEEN MY FIRM CONVICTION THAT SCOTLAND has a corner on ghosts. Her literature teems with instances of the supernatural, and Scottish superstition is proverbial.

Scottish folk whose roots are in the Highlands confess freely to a belief in the weird and the uncanny, and even the more practical-minded and down to earth Lowlanders will sometimes admit shamefacedly that "there may be something to it." Unbelievers and scoffers among the Scots may deny the existence of. . .

Bogles and ghaisties
And long-legged beasties
And things that go BOOMP!
In the night. . . .

but if pressed can often be induced to tell about something
"unco' uncanny" that happened—not to themselves, you'll
understand—but to the friend of an aunt of a connection of
a man they know.

My experience has been that if you scratch a Scotsman
you'll be pretty sure to find at least a bit of a belief in the
supernatural world under his skin, and that any Scottish
person you meet will be very likely to have a ghost story
somewhere up his sleeve.

I do not know whether the humorous ghost story is
peculiar to Scotland, but I do know that there are a lot of
them in Scottish ghostlore. Folks in these stories are always
having a terribly hard time with their ghosts, which perhaps
appeals to the very natural and human impulse to laugh at
the misfortunes of someone else, particularly when you are
comfortably sure that all will be well in the end. Perhaps,
too, the humorous ghost story comes into being because, in
spite of his much-talked-about dourness, the Scot really does
enjoy poking sly fun at himself.

The stories in GAELIC GHOSTS came out of the Highlands where scoffers and unbelievers are in a minority.

Unlike the *sgeulachdan* (skale-ak-tan), the unwritten impromptu tales of gifted story tellers and the Scottish tales of the fairy world, they did not emerge as full-fledged stories. They began as references that slipped now and then into the course of casual conversation, to "something that happened that was mortal queer," that the speaker is suddenly reminded of.

Take the tale of *Sandy MacNeil and His Dog*, for instance. An extravagant affection for dogs in our family had been handed down to us through long generations. This trait was so pronounced in my sister that although we were already well-supplied, she enticed dogs for miles around to accompany her home. A good bit of her free time was spent in returning them to their owners. A cousin of my grandmother, who visited us when we were children, took stock of the situation.

"You're just the cut o' Sandy MacNeil," he told her. "Happen you'll get a dog like his and hae his luck forbye."

We pounced on him and battered him with questions. Who was Sandy MacNeil? Och, naught but a lad who lived near Cairncraigie, the town our cousin was from. Why was he like my sister? Well, Sandy had a terrible fondness for dogs. Well, then, what happened to him? What was his luck? We had to tear the story away from him piecemeal, and put it together. What we had then was the story of Sandy and his big black dog.

9

Some of the stories in this book were gathered in the same way. Fragments of stories crept into conversations and had to be drawn out, bit by bit, by insistent questioning, and put together to make a whole. Quite often one person only knew part of the tale, and it took a long time to find someone to supply the missing parts. *The Giant Bones* needed three persons to complete it, and the *Walking Boundary Stone* needed two.

The Grateful Old Cailleach was told to me more or less as I have remembered it. I heard it years ago at a clan outing, and it was told to me by an old woman whose mother knew the wife of the farmer in Aberdeenshire to whom it happened.

Two of the stories are my own family possessions. It was a cousin of my father's father who had the experience at Culloden in *The Man o' the Clan*. When I raised the question of the MacDonalds not being in the battle that day I was told that they were on the field, which made their descendants eligible enough to see the Culloden ghosts. An uncle of my mother's great-aunt was the one who met *The Gambling Ghosts*. (That would be Wild Wully Anderson. Ye'll hae heard tell o' him.) Needless to say, we were always assured solemnly that these things really did occur, just as we heard them.

The House that Lacked a Bogle was some of my father's nonsense (so my mother said), and where he got the story I can't say. He had a fancy for collecting humorous ghost stories and knew a lot of them, which he told with imperturbable gravity and an apparently deep sympathy for the troubles of those involved in encounters with the ghosts.

When I was a child my mother's great-aunt told us the *Lady's Loaf-field*. It has the marks of a supernatural legend rather than a true ghost story. I think it must be very old. It has a medieval flavor.

The Holy Relic of Bannockburn is also a legend, and probably came out of one of the old monasteries. I have been told two versions, and prefer this one.

I had *The Old Laird and His Dogs* from an old man who had been a shepherd for the laird of one of the estates beyond Callander. He was a grand man with the bagpipes and could pipe the heart clean out of you when he played. After he grew too old and rheumaticky to keep the sheep any longer he came to America to stay with a married daughter, who lived not far from us when I was about half-grown. I had a hound's nose for a story so I soon tracked him down and got this one and a number of others from him.

That's the way the stories came to me; some in bits and pieces to be patched together, some from old story tellers now long dead, some handed down through the years by members of my own family. All of them were brought over the ocean and given to me. Old, well-remembered tales now come together in GAELIC GHOSTS.

cONTENTS

1   *Sandy MacNeil and His Dog* / 17

2   *The Giant Bones* / 30

3   *The Gambling Ghosts* / 39

4   *The Grateful Old Cailleach* / 46

5   *The Walking Boundary Stone* / 58

6   *The Lady's Loaf-field* / 68

7   *The Holy Relic of Bannockburn* / 76

8   *The Man o' the Clan* / 81

9   *The Old Laird and His Dogs* / 91

10 *The House that Lacked a Bogle* / 100

GAELIC GHOSTS

1 / SANDY MACNEIL AND HIS DOG

THERE ONCE WAS A MAN NAMED SANDY MacNEIL WHO
lived just outside of Cairncraigie. His family in the old days
had had plenty of lands and money, but that was in his
great-grandsire's time. Then the troubled times came along,
and when they were over, his great-grandsire was gone and
all the gold and gear had got themselves lost somehow, too.
So all that was handed down to Sandy were a few starve-crow
fields and an old tumble-down house.

Sandy was never one to mourn for what was gone and
long gone. He made do with what he had and managed to

scrape by on it. Being an easy-going, good-natured sort of a lad, he wasted no time complaining, and as he went his own gait and let his neighbors do the same he had plenty of friends and no enemies worth mentioning. All in all, he was as happy-go-lucky and contented as if he'd been a laird.

There was one queer thing about Sandy MacNeil. He had a terrible fancy for dogs, and they had the same for him. He'd be coming down to the village of a Saturday night, and every tyke in the town would prick up its ears and wag its tail as he passed by. Sandy'd go along to the tavern to have a friendly gab about the news of the week with whoever dropped in, and by the time he got there, a dozen or maybe more dogs would be footing it along before and behind him. Each one of them would be trying to shoulder the next one away to get closer to Sandy, and him talking away to them all the while. 'Twas a rare comical thing to see!

When Sandy came to the tavern door, he'd stop, and all the dogs would stop, too. Then Sandy would say polite-like, "That's all for now, laddies. Be off to your homes, for I cannot ask you in with me."

Then the dogs would wag their tails to show there was no offence taken, and off they'd go back to their homes, just as Sandy told them to do.

Some folks remarked that it was a queer thing entirely that Sandy MacNeil had no dog of his own. But others would say, why should he, when every other man's dog was just as much his as its master's. Still, the time came when Sandy did get a dog for himself, though the getting of it was no doing of his own.

This is the way it all came about.

One night Sandy was coming home from Cairncraigie. It was past nightfall, for he'd stayed longer than he meant to, the company being good and the talk entertaining. He was swinging along at a fair clip, because the morrow was the Sabbath, and there were chores that had to be done before midnight came so that he'd not be working on a Sunday.

It was a misty, cloudy sort of a night with a pale moon overhead that gave little light, being mostly behind a cloud. Besides, the road was dark because on either side there were tall hedges that cast their shadows on it. Maybe that's why Sandy didn't notice the dog. He did think once or twice that something was there, but he put it down to a fox or maybe a badger. Being in haste to get home, he paid it no heed.

It wasn't till he got to the place where the road met his own lane that he saw it. The hedge stopped there to let the lane through to the road. Just as Sandy got there the moon came peeping out for a minute from under the clouds. That was when he first caught sight of the dog.

Sandy had never seen its like before. The creature looked to be the size of a young calf, and it had long legs and a rough, shaggy coat of fur. From the point of its muzzle to 19 the tip of its tail it was black as coal. The moon went back behind the clouds then, so that was all that Sandy saw of it for the time. But the dog must have had its head turned toward Sandy, because he could see its eyes. The eyes shone with a bright red glow that made Sandy think of the way embers glow under the dead coals when a fire is about to go out.

Sandy was acquainted with all the dogs for miles around, and even from the little he'd seen of this dog he knew that it wasn't one of them. He never thought of being afraid, for he had yet to see the creature that could give him a fright. So he called the dog to come to him. The dog never made a move or a sound. It just stood there with those shining red eyes fixed on Sandy.

"Please yourself!" said Sandy, and he turned into the lane toward his house.

The dog came right along with him, keeping to its own side of the road and well away from Sandy. It was plain to see that it had no wish to be friendly. Sandy had great respect for the rights of dogs, as well as of men, so he let it be.

When Sandy got up to his house, the dog was still there. "Now lad," said Sandy. "'Tis sure you've come a long ways from your home, for if you lived near I'd be knowing you. By that same token, you've a long journey to go before you get home again. You'd best be off and away!"

But the minute Sandy opened the door the dog slipped by him into the house.

"Och now!" cried Sandy. "Come out o' there, my lad! Where'er you belong, 'tis not here."

But the dog did not come out and, what with the house so dark and the dog so black, Sandy couldn't see where it was at all.

Sandy went in and found a lamp. He lit it, and then he looked about for the dog. He found it lying on the bench by the fire in the front room. It lay with its nose down on its paws, and its eyes gleaming at Sandy with the same red glow. Now that Sandy could look at it by lamplight, he could see what a huge creature it was. He'd vow it was twice the size of any he'd e'er seen before. But it wasn't its uncommon size that gave Sandy a queer sort of feeling, but something else about it that Sandy couldn't put into words.

However, dogs were dogs, and Sandy was fond of them all. So he said, "Well then, lie there. Rest yourself a bit if you like. Happen you're weary, poor creature."

Sandy went about getting things ready for the morn. When he'd finished his chores and filled the kettle and laid out his Sunday clothes, he said coaxingly, "Come away now, black laddie! 'Tis time for you to be off to where you belong."

He opened the house door for the dog to go out. The dog made no move to go, but lay still upon the bench. Sandy was used to having dogs do what he told them to do, and it surprised him that this one didn't mind him.

"Happen he's deaf!" he told himself. So he went over to the dog to give it a nudge off the bench. He laid his hand on the dog's shoulder. There was no feeling of flesh or fur under his hand and his fingers came down flat on the bench!

Sandy snatched his hand away as if he'd burnt it. A shiver ran up his spine and back down again. Then he laughed at himself. Half asleep on his feet he must be, and dreaming! It was late and he must be more tired than he'd thought. He went and took the lamp up from the table, carried it over to the fire, and leaned over the bench to take a good look at the dog. He nearly dropped the lamp! He wasn't dreaming! Losh! 'Twas no proper dog there at all! *'Twas the ghost of a dog!*

Sandy backed away. He set the lamp down on the table, his fingers trembling so that it was all he could do to put it upright. Then he sat down to think it over. Of one thing he was sure. He'd not tamper with the creature any further. So the dog lay and looked at Sandy, and Sandy looked at the dog.

What the dog was thinking about a body couldn't tell. At first, Sandy couldn't think at all, but after a while his wits came back to him, and he started to reason the matter out. Ghost or not, the dog appeared to mean him no harm. Sandy told himself that if he were going to be haunted at all, he'd rather be haunted by the ghost of a dog than many another he could think of. His great-grandsire, for one, who'd have made a raring ranting old bogle from all that Sandy'd ever heard tell of him. Anyhow, the ghost was there and meant to stay, so what could Sandy do about it? Having come to this conclusion, Sandy told himself that a man needed his rest. So he blew out the lamp and went to bed. And after a while he got off to sleep.

When he woke in the morn he laughed to himself. "Och!" he said, "That was a rare fine dream I was having the night's night." And he went yawning down the stairs to put the kettle over the fire for his morning tea. He looked over at the bench as he passed by the front-room door, just sort of making sure it was a dream.

The dog was still there!

Right then and there Sandy made up his mind.

"If I can't drive you out," he said to the dog, "neither shall you drive me out. 'Tis my house and I'm staying in it. The place is big enough for the two of us."

So the dog stayed with Sandy, and Sandy stayed with the dog. At first, Sandy had an eerie feeling seeing it lying there as he came in and out of the house, knowing what it was. But that soon wore off, and he paid it no heed at all. To tell the truth, after a week or two he began to like having it there. It was company for him, living alone as he did.

Except for the night he met it on the road, Sandy never saw it anywhere but on the bench by the fire, although some-

times, as he came up the lane, he had a fancy that it was
walking beside him. But when he came into the house, it
was always there on the bench.

Sandy never told folks he had a dog, but it wasn't long
till they found out for themselves. They found out what sort
of a dog it was, too.

One evening, a neighbor of Sandy's stopped by to ask
for the loan of some tool or other, and when Sandy stepped
out of the house to give it to him, he left the door standing
open.

While Sandy stood on the doorstep talking to him, the
man—being the sort that is always curious about other folks—
peered into the room. He saw the great black dog lying on
the bench by the fire.

"Och then!" said the man. "You've got yourself a dog
at last, Sandy MacNeil."

"Happen I have," Sandy said.

"'Tis an odd-looking creature!" the man exclaimed,
leaning to look past Sandy.

"Happen it is," said Sandy, and he reached behind himself to pull the door to.

The neighbor had a lot more curiosity than he had wits.
"I'll just have a look at it then," he said, pushing past Sandy
into the room.

"I'd not advise it." Sandy warned him. But the man was
already across the room and had his hand on the dog.

24

The haste with which the man left Sandy's house was amazing. He screeched something at Sandy as he flew past, but what it was Sandy could never tell. Before Sandy could tell him the dog would do him no harm, he was out of sight.

To be sure, the news spread like fire in dry corn stubble. Soon there wasn't anybody that didn't know that Sandy had got a dog for himself that was the ghost of a dog.

It nearly turned the village upside down. Some folks said nothing at all and some said they'd not go near Sandy MacNeil's house for love nor money. But there was an awful sluagh of folks that took it upon themselves to give Sandy a word of advice.

Sandy was used to going his own gait and didn't like being interfered with, so he gave this lot the rough edge of his tongue.

"'Tis no concern of yours what kind of a dog I've got," he said angrily.

"Ye'd do well to get rid of it," they insisted.

"Get rid of it!" Sandy said hotly. "Och, why should I do that?"

"'Tis unnatural entirely, a dog's ghaist," they said.

"It does no harm," Sandy insisted.

"Not yet," said they.

"Nor ever will," retorted Sandy. "He suits me fine! Not a penny does he cost me, for he doesn't need to be fed or tended. Nor does he keep folks awake o' nights baying at the

moon like the tykes of some folks I could be naming. He can
bide with me as long as he likes, so hauld your whisht!''

The truth was that, ghost or no ghost, the dog was
Sandy's dog and he'd got terrible fond of it.

What he minded most was that folks wouldn't stop
havering about it. It was all they talked about at the tavern
and a man could find no comfort there any more. It was just
as bad when they met him on the road or in the village. Nobody could find anything to talk about but the big black dog
that was a ghost and that was going to bring Sandy terrible
bad luck.

One Saturday evening he came home from the village
and sat down to take off his boots by the fire. He'd come
away extra early, because he couldn't see any sense in staying
there because of the way they all kept nattering at him.

He looked over to the dog and said to it, ''If it's any
sort o' luck you're going to bring me, be at it and let's have
done with it! Either that or do something to stop their
blethering, for I'm weary of hearing them go on about it.''

And being so put out and upset by it all, he did what
he'd never have done to a dog had he not been driven to it.
He took the boot he had in his hand and hurled it at the dog.

The boot never went near the dog, for which Sandy was
glad, because he'd never meant to throw it.

''Och, lad!'' said he to the dog. ''Tis sorry I am!''

But the dog looked at him for a minute with its eyes   27

glowing redder than ever, and then it leaped down from the bench and up the stairs. Sandy ran after to see what it was up to, but the dog had too much of a start on him. Just as Sandy got to the top of the stairs the dog gave a great bound that took it right through the wall. Where it went through, it left behind a great hole in the wall, and Sandy ran over to see if he could find out where the dog had gone.

When Sandy got to the hole, he found that it wasn't a hole at all. Instead it was a hidden cupboard that he had never known was there, because it was behind the plaster that had long ago been laid over it. The door of the cupboard stood open now, and while Sandy stood and stared at it a great bag fell off the shelf and dinged down on the floor. The bag flew open, and out poured a great stream of golden coins.

Sandy fell onto his knees before it. "Luck!" he cried. "Och, here's all the luck in the world! And 'twas my big black dog that brought it to me!"

It was his great-grandsire's gold that had gotten itself lost, because he had hidden it away there before he went off to fight in the troubled times. Since he'd got himself killed, he never came back to tell them where it was.

Sandy gathered the gold up into a basket and took it down to the village to show folks the kind of luck the ghost of the big black dog had brought him. The ones who had the most to say before were the very ones who had the least

to say when they saw the gold.

The sorry thing for Sandy was that he never saw the dog again, and he missed it sorely. He waited long for it to come back, and there were times he told himself he'd rather have it than all his great-grandsire's gold. But at last he gave up waiting and got himself a tyke to keep him company. It wasn't as big or black or quiet as the other, but it helped.

Now that Sandy was the richest man in the countryside, folks took to calling him The MacNeil, to show their respect. He found himself a bonnie young wife and built himself a fine new house, which he called "Dog's Luck" just to remind folks where his money came from.

He still goes into the village of a Saturday night, and if you should be there and see a man with a dozen or more dogs footing it along before and behind him, each trying to shoulder the next one out of the way to get closer to him, you'll know that's Sandy MacNeil.

2 / THE   GIANT   BONES

ONCE IN THE OLD, OLD DAYS LONG SINCE GONE, THERE
dwelt a race of giants in the land of Caledonia, which was the
name folks had for Scotland then. What ever happened to
them nobody knows, although many an old tale is told about
it. Some say they went along with Angus Og when he went
away with the weight of sorrow on his shoulders because of
the evil doings of man. Some will tell you the giant folk
battled among themselves until they had all killed each other
off. And there are still others who will tell you that a great
beast rose up from the sea and ate all of them up. They're

all grand stories, and you can believe what you like and no one will be faulting you for it, because no one will know any more about it than yourself. One thing is certain: Gone they are, the whole lot of them, and naught left behind them but some huge bones that show what big-sized creatures they were when they walked about in their flesh.

They say these bones are to be found in a great cave near the causeway at the far northern tip of Scotland. The man who found them first ran off screaming. He never was the same again, for he swore that as he bent over to look at what might have been a knucklebone—and it half as big as himself—he gave it a sharp rap with the toe of his boot. It was all by accident, for he didn't mean to at all. And, according to the way he tells the story, something moved across the cave, and a great voice roared at him.

"Och now!" it said. "Will ye not take heed to yourself, wee man o' the people, that ye'll not be disturbing honest folk in their sleep!"

The man looked all around him and all around the cave. He could see plain enough by the light from the sea waves, where the sun danced upon them near the opening that there was nobody in the place but himself alone. But he could *feel* that there was something there, and it was coming right at him! 'Twas then he screamed and ran away.

As it was the most important event of his life, he told the tale of it over and over, and is still telling it to whoever

will stop to listen, for all anyone knows. But one thing he'd never tell and that was where the cave with the giant bones was to be found. He had a dread on him that the telling of it would set whatever it was in the cave after him.

Folks that dwelt thereabouts got used to his story and finally they got tired of it. But he was always able to find someone to listen to it, because the place he lived in was a grand one for the hunting and fishing folk from below the border who came up for their holidays. That way, it wasn't hard to find a new pair of ears that hadn't heard him tell about the cave with the giant bones.

Well, at last he told the tale to a man who was new to the place and had never even been in Scotland before. This stranger was one of those fellows who work at gathering fossils and old bones and the like, and looking into ruined places to find out what sort of folks had belonged to them maybe hundreds of years ago. When he found out enough, he'd make a book out of his knowledge and people would buy the book and pay good money for it. Which was why he wrote it, of course.

When the stranger heard about the giant bones, he was bound to make a book about them. The trouble was that nobody but the man who had found them knew where they were, and he wasn't telling.

The stranger flew into a rage and said nobody need tell him, for he'd just find the cave for himself.

33

Well, he searched up and he searched down all along the seacoast, and he found a terrible lot of caves; but not one of the lot had any sort of bones except those of sea birds in it, nor anything else that would have paid him back for the time he'd spent looking.

Finally, there wasn't so much as a hole in a rock he hadn't looked into, and he'd take his oath that there wasn't a cave anywhere that he'd missed. There was a suspicion in his mind that the whole story was a pack o' nonsense all made up in the mind of the man who'd told it to him.

He climbed up to the top of the cliff and began to walk back toward the place where he was staying. It was easier walking up there than over the shale along the shore. Climbing in and out of caves had made him hot and weary, and he was awful mad because he thought he'd been made a fool of. He was walking along, with his mind busy with what he was going to say to the man whose story had sent him after the bones, so maybe he wasn't watching where he was going. At any rate, all of a sudden the ground crumbled under him, and down he shot over the cliff's edge in the midst of a great shower of dirt and stones.

He landed on a great heap of rubble with the breath knocked clean out of him. He soon found he wasn't hurt bad, so as soon as he got his breath back he sat up to see where he was. The sea came up to the foot of the pile of stuff he was sitting on and at either side of him was a great boulder

34

towering halfway up the cliff. But it wasn't the boulders that held his eye. Between the two of them was the opening to a cave. He'd never seen either boulders or opening before, and he couldn't see how he'd missed them, but he wasted no time trying to figure out why. Up he got and into the cave he ran.

It was the right one! There were the giant bones lying all over the floor just as the man had told him.

'Twas the sight to gladden the eye of one who earned his bread poking his nose into old bones and the like. He started at once to sort them out, figuring that if he could get a whole man laid out 'twould make a grand picture for the book he was going to write. So being busy at it, he paid no heed to anything else, until a great rumbling voice roared in his ears, and the voice said, *"Leave the bones be, man!"*

Losh! The stranger leaped a foot in the air for fright. When he came down, he tripped over one of the bones he'd been sorting out and landed with a thump on a couple more. And another thundering voice shouted, "Och, ye clumsy lout! Will you not stop booting my poor old bones about!"

The stranger was so near dead with fright that he scarce had the strength to lift his head to see who was speaking. When he did, he'd have been better pleased if he'd not looked at all. All around the cave, reaching all the way from the floor to the top of it, stood a ring of ghosts. They were the biggest ghosts anyone ever saw. The cave was so big you

could have drilled a regiment in it easy and with room to spare; but they made it feel crowded, they were that huge.

There was no place he could run because he was in the midst of them, and they gathered around him as they were, shoulder to shoulder and toe to toe. So he lay there looking up at them, with his blood grueing and himself shaking like a leaf in the wind.

"What shall we do wi' the wee sma' man?" roared one of the great ghosts.

"Crock him!" answered another, in a voice that nearly split the stranger's lugs.

"Let me at him!" shouted a third of them. "I'll be taking him apart, so I will, to spread his wee bones amongst our own. 'Twas my shin he was knocking a while back, so it was!"

"Och nay!" thundered the biggest of them all. "Would we be having the puny wee bones of him cluttering up the place? Let's be rid of him!"

"Let's be rid of him!" they all agreed, and their combined voices bouncing around the cave sounded like thunder along mountain tops.

Before the stranger could get himself to his knees to beg for mercy, he felt something pick him up, and there was a great swirling and booming. Out of the cave he flew, as if carried by a whirlwind, spinning like a top through the air, and into the sea he fell.

He'd have drowned, if it had not been for some fishermen who heard the splash he made. They turned their boats, came up to him, and fished him out of the sea more dead than alive.

When they brought him to, he tried to tell them about the terrible experience he'd had. But they only laughed at him and told him that people getting drowned always had strange fancies afterward. He'd fallen into the sea from the cliff above. That was all.

The stranger never wrote the book, for he had no wish to be poking his nose into those bones again. But the story spread around, and curious people went to look for the cave. They never found it. All they found was the two huge boulders, and they were set close together, and half of them buried in the cliff. Some people said it was plain to be seen they'd been that way a hundred years or more. Some people said the giant ghosts had pushed them there to bar the door of the cave so they could rest in peace. However it was, you can go and look at the place yourself. They'll show you the boulders and tell you there's a cave behind them full of giant ghosts guarding their giant bones.

3 / THE GAMBLING GHOSTS

THERE WAS A LAD ONCE WHO WAS TAKEN WITH A PASSION for gambling. He wasn't a bad sort of a lad at all, only heedless. He had come into a bit of money from an old uncle, and it was like to be the ruin of him. Now that he thought he had his fortune made, he left off working entirely, and spent all his time from morn till late at night in the nearby town, playing cards and rattling dice and betting on anything at all with anyone who was willing to take him up on it. Sometimes he lost, but he won often enough to make him want to try again, being sure he'd double his fortune that way.

His mother and father were good respectable folks, and it grieved them sorely to have such a son to put up with, but naught they could say would make him mend his ways. He just went along, gambling and gaming. That is, for a while at least.

One fine day, having slept till noon because he'd come in very late the night before, he got up to get himself ready to go back to the town. He'd bought himself a fine new suit of clothes the day before, so he put them on and away he went very much pleased with himself. He found himself on a winning streak that day, and with things going well, he'd won all the money of everyone he played with before midnight rolled around. The ones he had played with couldn't play with him any more, and the others wouldn't, so he decided there was nothing better for him to do than go home and catch up on the sleep he'd lost the night before. So off he went with his pockets full of other folks' silver and gold going chink-a-tink-tink and making a merry tune for him as he walked along.

There was a short cut to his home which made the way half as long as if he went round by the road. Many a man would not have taken it, because it lay across a lonely grave-yard, but this cantie lad was afraid of naught, so he took it and came to the graveyard shortly before the midnight hour.

There was a bright moon riding the sky above, and it

showed the graveyard plain, with the headstones standing up tall and white and the trees around the graveyard pointing black shadows at them.

Right in the middle of the place was a huge square old gravestone lying flat on the ground to mark the place where some grand person or other was buried. When the gambling lad came to the stone he looked at it, and it came into his mind that it looked uncommonly like a gaming table, being raised up as it was quite a bit above the ground. Maybe it was the tune the money played in his pocket or maybe some wicked spirit of mischief got hold of him, but whatever it was, he was so possessed by it that he leaped up to the middle of the stone and danced a fling.

And he chanted:

> *I'm Willie Wassle;*
> *I'm in me castle,*
> *Not a man in all the town*
> *Dares pull Willy Wassle down!*

And then he shouted out. "Och, if the living will not play with me, I'll just play with the dead! So come out, me lads!"

And all of a sudden, four white figures rose up around him, one at each side of the gravestone. *And they were ghosts!*

42   The poor lad stood there shaking in his fine new boots.

He'd got what he was asking for, and he didn't like it at all.

He made ready to jump from the stone and take to his heels, but he couldn't, for the ghost that stood at the head of the gravestone reached out and caught him by the ankle. So there he had to stay, with his hair on end and his teeth fleckering in his jaws, and hardly knowing whether he was alive or dead himself.

"We'll not be playing *with* you, my lad," said the ghost that had him by the ankle and seemed to be the leader of them all. "But we'll play for what you've got."

And the other ghosts cried out, "Aye that we will! We'll play for what you've got." And all four of them screeched out a laugh that was horrible to hear.

"We'll play for the gold and silver in your pockets first," said the ghost at the head of the stone, and he pulled out a pair of dice that looked suspiciously like old dead bones, and threw them out before him. The four of them began to play, and soon they'd played the silver and gold right out of the poor lad's pockets.

Then they sat back and looked at him. "What'll we play for next?" one of them asked.

"I've an awful fancy for his jacket," another one answered. "I like it fine."

So they played for his fine new jacket, and soon they had that off his back. Then they played for his plaidie and his vest and his kilt and his Hieland bonnet, and they got them all.

43

They played for his sporran and his belt and his hose and his garters and his fine buckled shoes, and he had to give them up. They even played for his sgian-dhu, the bonny little dirk that he carried in his hose, and when they had them all, they looked him over again, considering.

"There's not much left that's worth the game," said one of them to another. "What can we try for next?"

The poor lad stood there barefooted and barelegged, shivering in the cold night air, with nothing left but his undershirt and his trews.

"Och, then," said the ghost at the head of the stone, as he reached out to pick up the dice, "we can play for his soul!"

"That you'll not!" screamed the lad. The terror of the words the ghost had spoken gave such wings to the lad's feet that he leaped from the stone clean over their heads and into the midst of the gravestones six rows away. He tore off and out of the graveyard, up through the woods and over the fields, and never looked back to see if they came after.

He fell in at the door of his own house just as the cock crew for daybreak. He knew he was safe then, so he fell to the floor with no more strength left than a newborn lamb and fainted dead away. His mother found him lying there when she came down to put the kettle on for the morning's tea, and she didn't know what to make of it.

44   The lad was a changed person after that terrible night.

He left off gambling entirely and settled down to a steady job, saving his money and going to church twice of a Sunday. He became a real credit to his family, and all because he'd met up with those four gambling ghosts.

THERE WAS A MAN ONCE WHO HAD A RARE GIFT FOR BEING
happy. As he never looked for trouble before it came, or
looked back upon it when it was past, he went through life
with a heart as light as duck's down. Being happy himself, he
liked to have everybody else happy too; so he did what he
could to make sure they were. Anyone in trouble went to him
as straight as a bee seeks a blossom, for they knew he'd always
be ready with a kind word and a helping hand when they were
needed.

46   It wasn't that he had so much to be happy about, because

he was naught but a poor farmer, and many a neighbor had more than he did. But those that had more very often got less pleasure out of theirs than he did out of the little he could call his own.

So although his bit of a cottage wasn't much for size it was full of happiness from wall to wall and roof to floor. His wife went about her work singing, and his bonnie wee lass and his fine young laddie were as merry as if the world were made for them.

Some folks said 'twas all well enough to give when you had plenty left for yourself, but it was a daft thing to take what you could ill spare to give to folks who were no kin at all.

"Och," he laughed, "I give little because I have little, but I can always find someone worse off than myself."

One windy autumn eve toward lamplighting time, his wife stopped by the window to look out at the weather as she went to get the light from the chimney shelf.

A misty chill rain was falling, and the fields were brown and drear.

"Och!" she exclaimed, "have a look out there now! There's a poor old cailleach coming up the road in the rain and the cold and all."

Her husband came beside her to look into the road. "The poor old soul!" he cried. "What with the night coming on and the weather so bad, 'tis no time for her to be trudging

47

along alone." And he said to his son, "Run out, laddie, and fetch the old woman into the house."

The lad ran out and fetched the old woman in. They set her in a warm corner by the fire. The wee lass put a cup of hot tea in her hand, and the farmer stirred up the fire to dry her wet skirts quicker. The laddie unlaced her boots and stood them away from the blaze to dry by the hearth, and the wife fetched her own shawl and laid it over the old woman's shoulders. And all the time they kept on talking to her and around her, and laughed as they ran about doing this and that to make her comfortable. 'Tis no wonder she didn't feel strange, but as if she were a welcome guest that they'd all been expecting.

They soon drew her story from her. She'd lost her place in the city because she was too old and lacked strength to do the work. She had a good son up this way, and he and his wife had been at her for a long time to come and bide with them, so that's where she was going. She'd taken the railway to the market town, intending to walk the rest of the way, but she hadn't counted on the weather being so bad.

"But why didn't they come to fetch you?" asked the farmer's wife gently when she learned where the son lived. "'Tis a long way there, even from here."

"To be sure, they'd have done so, had I asked them," the old woman said. "But I came so quickly, there wasn't time to let them know."

"Och well," said the farmer, "you'll bide with us for the night, and if you're rested tomorrow we'll put you on your way."

So when they had eaten their supper, they tucked her in for the night in the wee lass's bed, and made up a pallet for the lassie beside her.

The next morn, the farmer hitched his mare to the cart to take the old woman to her son. The farmer's wife wrapped the old woman in the shawl she had put about her the night before because, although the rain had stopped, the air was damp and chill and the way before them long.

The farmer's wife came out to see them off, and as they started away, the old woman said, "You've been kind as heaven itself to me. I can't think what I'd have done, had you not taken me in. I doubt there's much an old cailleach like myself can ever do in return, but if there's ever anything, be sure I'll do it."

Well, the autumn went by, and the winter too, and spring came after. The old cailleach was almost forgotten, for the farmer and his family had to do for themselves, and it kept them all busy. There was little time to be thinking of things that happened so long ago.

A day came when the farmer had to go into the market town. His wife came out to the road to see him off, and she looked up at the sky with an anxious frown. "I doubt there'll be a storm today," said she.

"Happen there will," he agreed. "But I may miss it, one way or another. It may not come before I get back, and if it does, 'twill likely be over before I start for home. I've put the canvas top on the cart against the storm if it comes."

"'Tis sure to be dark in any case," said his wife. "Night comes on early, and it is dark still earlier when the weather is bad." She laid her hands on the reins as he gathered them up ready to start.

"Promise you'll take the long way round when you'll be coming home," she said earnestly. "I do not like the short road, even by day and in good weather. The brig over the burn on it is a terrible dangerous place to travel over."

The farmer smiled down at her. "Dinna fash yourself, lass." he said. "'Tis not your way to worrit and fret without cause. I'll be wanting the hot supper you'll have waiting for me, so make sure it's a good one."

And off he went, and it wasn't until he was out of sight she remembered that he'd not given her the promise she'd asked for.

The farmer reached the town in time, but the business he had come to attend to took longer than he'd expected. Before he'd got it finished and was started back home, the storm which had been threatening all day struck with all its force. Storm or no storm, he thought, as the mare splashed along through the puddles, he'd have to take the short way or he'd never get home in time for his supper.

The short way was a hard rough road, and the old wooden bridge above the burn was rickety and narrow. The bed of the stream was far below under the bridge, and its course was full of sharp, cruel rocks. Should a man miss the bridge in the dark and the rain, he'd get hurt bad, if nothing worse. But the farmer told himself he'd be going slow and careful, so there was nothing to fear. The long way was smoother, and the burn came down near the town with a good strong bridge of stone over it. But losh! the farmer said to himself, he'd be an hour longer, or maybe more, getting home if he took the long road. He'd been away from home long enough now, and he wanted the supper his wife would have ready for him. He'd be taking the short way home this night.

When he turned his horse away from the town into the country road, he thought he saw someone standing by the side of the road ahead. As he came up beside the waiting figure, a flash of lightning lit its face and he saw it plain.

"Losh!" he cried, "'tis the old cailleach! Come away into the cart! 'Twill be some shelter for you, though the way it pours, 'tis none too dry."

The old woman climbed into the cart, and he pulled out some sacks from under the seat to spread over her knees.

"You choose bad weather for your journeys," he said, "so now you will have to pay us another visit. Well, you'll be more than welcome, to be sure. We'll all be glad to hear how you've been faring."

"I knew you were in the town," said the old woman. "I was waiting for you."

He thought it was strange she knew he was in town, but then maybe she'd seen him there.

"Had you sent me word," he told her, "I'd have been glad to come by for you. Then you could have waited under cover."

She murmured something. Probably a word of thanks, he thought.

"Had you been waiting long?" the farmer asked anxiously. "Are you not wet through?"

He wondered if he should turn back to the town and have her get her clothes dried and get her a cup of hot tea to warm her.

"Nay," she replied. "Not long. Not long. And I'm not wet at all."

His mind relieved by her answer, the farmer gave his attention to the mare, which was slowly picking its way along with its head down against the storm. It was all he could do to keep the cart to the road, with the rain coming down in sheets and the lightning blinding the horse and himself at every flash.

So he and the old cailleach went along without talking at all, until they got to the fork in the road where the long way home went one way and the short way went the other.

He turned the cart into the shorter road as he had made

up his mind to do, but before the horse had stepped more than two or three paces the old woman rose up in the seat beside him, and reaching over him laid her hand on the reins.

"Nay! Nay! Nay!" she cried as she gripped them fast. "You must not go by the short road! Take the other way!"

He was half-frightened by the suddenness of her action and the wild sound of her voice, but he said gently, "Och come, come now! We'll be on our way an hour or more longer if we go the long way home. It will be a long pull the short way, with the rain the way it is."

But, over and over again, she cried, "You must take the long way home!"

She was so old and frail, he'd never have thought her grip on the reins could be so strong. He did not want to be rough with her, and besides he was afraid if he insisted, she might refuse to go on with him. She'd catch her death of a cold for sure, if she got out into the rain.

So, to humor her he said, "Och well! We'll go the other way, then."

As soon as he said it she took her hand from the reins. He backed the cart and turned it into the longer road.

After they had started off on the longer way, the old cailleach said nothing more. Indeed, she seemed to have fallen asleep in the corner, leaning against the support over which the canvas top was stretched.

They went on in silence then, through the wind and the 55

rain, and at last they reached home. The old woman still leaned back in the shadows of the corner of the seat.

"She's sleeping yet," the farmer said to himself. "I'll leave her be while I go fetch a shawl to wrap her in, before I carry her into the house."

His wife threw open the door when she heard his step on the path. She flew down the steps and threw herself into his arms.

"You're back!" she cried. "And you're safe! You're safe!" And she burst into tears.

"Och I'm back," he told her, "and I'm safe to be sure. Come, lass, hush your greeting. I'm sorry I'm late, but I took the long way after all. Run and fetch me a shawl, for I've got the old cailleach that was here before out in the cart and I want to wrap her up to bring her in."

His wife drew back and stared at him with wide eyes. *"The old cailleach?"* she asked.

"That I do," said he. "I picked her up from the side of the road just outside of the town."

Then his wife told him. "The old cailleach's son stopped by today, just after you left. He thanked us for caring for his mother that night she came by last year. And he told me the brig had fallen down into the burn on the short road. Och! I've been near mad all day for fear you'd come that way and fall down on the rocks, not knowing the brig wasn't there because of the dark and the storm."

"Do you say so!" exclaimed the farmer. "Well, lass, you can thank the old woman for that. I was set on taking the short road home, but she took the reins and held them till I told the old lass I'd go the longer way. She was bound I should not take the short road, and 'twas well she was, for I'd never have seen the bridge was gone."

"Nay," said his wife, "that cannot be. For the old body's son told me today that his mother was dead and in her grave this fortnight back."

The farmer wouldn't believe her until he had gone out and looked into the cart to make sure the old woman wasn't there. All he found was a heap of sacks against the support that held the canvas top of the cart.

"The good old body!" he said slowly and soberly to his wife. "Do you mind how she said, when I was taking her to her son, that if ever there was aught she could do to repay us she'd be sure to do it? Och, lass, she's kept her promise, for I'd not be standing here if she hadn't made me come the long way home. But she had to come from her grave to do it."

And so she had.

THERE ONCE WERE TWO OLD CROFTERS NAMED JAMIE MacNAB
and Rab MacRae, whose farms lay alongside of each other.
Each of these old fellows had a good flock of sheep, good
fields for growing corn and for grazing, and a good sound
house. Each of them also had a good wife and a good son,
and since they were hard working and thrifty, they didn't
lack for a bit of gold and gear. Neither of them could boast
of having more than the other, so neither of them had any
reason to wish himself in the other's shoes. For that reason,
they were the best of friends.

Where their lands met at the high road there was a huge square stone. Half of the stone was on Rab MacRae's land and the other half on Jamie MacNab's, so the middle of it marked where one farm left off and the other one began. Both the MacNabs and the MacRaes were uncommonly proud of the stone, each family owning half of it, as you might say. It was terribly ancient, having been there since the beginning of time, and it had always belonged to MacNabs and MacRaes. Everybody called it the Boundary stone.

When the day's work was over, if the weather was fine, the two old crofters liked to walk down to the road in the gloaming and sit on the stone, each on his own side. Maybe they'd talk, or maybe they'd just sit there quiet and peaceful-like, but it gave them great satisfaction.

Well, in time the two old crofters died and were laid away to rest in the churchyard down over the hill. Their two good sons took over, and now they each had the good flock of sheep and the good fields and the good sound house, all of which was left them by their fathers. And each of them had a good wife and a good son, both of which they'd got for themselves.

Their two young lads were called Young Jamie MacNab and Young Rab MacRae, both having been named for their grandsires.

Of course, the two old crofters' sons each had their half of the Boundary stone. They worked hard and laid a bit by, and they took their rest together of a fine evening on the stone just as their fathers had done before them. They, too, grew old and died and were laid away to rest in the church-yard down over the hill.

Then it was the turn of Young Jamie MacNab and Young Rab MacRae to take over. Both of them were as good lads as you'd hope to find in a long day's journey. They were as hard working and thrifty as the MacNabs and MacRaes had ever been, and they'd been friends since they were born. With all that, and the example of their fathers and their grandsires to guide them, all should have gone well.

Now 'tis a sure thing that when trouble comes between two friends it is always a third person sets it going, and so it was in this case. The cause of the trouble, strange enough, was the Boundary Stone.

It all started when Young Jamie MacNab met old Sandy MacBean by the stone one morn. Jamie was out looking for a teg that had strayed away from the rest of his sheep when old Sandy hailed him.

Jamie was in a terrible hurry to find the teg, but Sandy was such an old man that Jamie paid him the courtesy of waiting a bit. After they had passed the time of day and talked of this and that old Sandy said, "A-well, Jamie, I see someone's been shiftin' the old Boundary stone."

Jamie took a look at the stone. "'Tis as it was, far as I can see," said he.

"Nay, Jamie," old Sandy said stubbornly. "I'm pushin' ninety year, and I'm tellin' ye that stone should be closer to the burn by twenty foot. My memory's as long as my years, and there's little I've forgot. 'Tis so the stone was in your grandsire's day and 'tis so it should be now."

Jamie looked at the stream, and then he took another look at the stone. "Maybe so," he said doubtfully. "Happen 'twould be the road menders moved it. I never gave heed to it." After all, Jamie thought, Sandy MacBean was very likely right. He was a great hand at remembering things everyone else forgot. "I'll get an ox and a chain and shift it back," said Jamie.

Now Sandy MacBean did have a prodigious memory, but what slipped his mind this time was the great storm which swept over Scotland before Young Jamie was ever born. It wasn't the stone that had been shifted, but the stream. The heavy rains had cut a new bed for it beyond the old one and left the stone high and dry and full twenty feet away. Sandy MacBean forgot that entirely. Down there was the burn and up here was the stone, and they ought to be together. That's what old Sandy MacBean said.

Sandy MacBean went off, terribly pleased with the wonderful memory he had, and Jamie fetched the ox and the chain and hauled the stone down the road until it was twenty feet closer to the stream.

That night, when the two friends met by the road,

Young Rab MacRae let out a whistle. "Losh!" he cried in surprise. "Who's been shifting the stone then?"

"'Twas me," said Jamie.

"What way would you do so?" asked Rab.

"Sandy MacBean said it was always down there near the stream," Jamie told him. "The road menders must have shifted it."

"But 'tis over on my land now," Rab protested.

"That it isn't," said Jamie. "'Tis between your land and mine."

"'Tis not!" said Rab. "'Tis on my land and I'll take it kindly if you'll shift it back again!"

"I'll not do it!" shouted Jamie. "Sandy MacBean says . . ."

"The de'il take old Sandy MacBean!" Rab shouted right back at him. "I'll shift it back my own self!"

So the two of them turned their backs to each other and walked away. Rab went and got one of his oxen and a chain and shifted the stone up the road to where it was in the first place.

After that, Rab MacRae shifted the stone up the road away from the burn on Mondays, Wednesdays, and Fridays, and Jamie MacNab shifted it back down the road on Tuesdays, Thursdays, and Saturdays. On Sunday, which was the Lord's Day, when neither of them dared lay hand on the stone to shift it, they sat and glowered at each other in

63

church while the dominie preached at them about loving their neighbor, to which neither of them paid any heed at all.

There was no more sitting on the stone of an evening, side by side.

Jamie and Rab stalked off to the tavern in the village to find company, and when they found each other there, they took great care to pretend they didn't see each other at all.

Things went on that way for quite a while, with the stone traveling up and down regular-like. Then, one night Rab stood up and said he was tired of the whole business and that he'd shift the stone no more. Folks at the tavern had been taking sides and laying bets on who'd win in the end; but Jamie told them no matter what Rab said, they'd better not settle their bets yet. For his part, he was going to wait and see if Rab meant it or not.

He'd hauled the stone down to the burn that day, so the next morning he went down to have a look. He was half hoping the stone would be where he'd put it, because he was tired of the quarrel too, to tell the truth. But the stone had been moved, so what could he do but haul it back to the stream again? If Rab wouldn't give up, no more would he! But, after another week of it, Jamie could stand no more.

He told folks at the tavern that it was queer enough that every time he got the stone down by the burn it was back up by the road the next morning. And Rab got mad and said he'd not laid a hand on the stone for the past week, and that, for all he knew, Jamie was amusing himself, hauling it back and forth just to make it look as if Rab was doing it. They almost came to blows and maybe they would have, if just at the moment, something hadn't stopped them. The door flew open and in rushed old Sandy MacBean. There was no doubt about it. Sandy was in a terrible taking, for his white hair stood up on his head and his face was as white as his hair.

"Lads!" he cried in his old cracked voice. "Lads! I come by yon stone of Jamie's and Rab's the noo, and it's *walking.*"

Jamie and Rab forgot their fight entirely. Out the door and up the road they tore, side by side. When they got there, they both stopped in their tracks. They clutched each other, and lucky they did, for neither of them could have stood up alone, they was so taken with fright.

Because the stone *was* walking.

There was two pair of legs at each corner, shuffling along under the stone.

"Och, I've gone daft," groaned Jamie.

"Me too," moaned Rab.

Just at that moment the stone began to settle down right in the place it had stood before Old Sandy MacBean had started all the shifting. Out from under the corners of the stone stepped four ghosts. They were the ghosts of Grandsire MacNab and Grandsire MacRae, and their two good sons

65

who were the fathers of Young Jamie and Young Rab. And all of them were terribly cross.

The four of them lined up in a row and looked sternly at Young Jamie and Young Rab, while the two lads stood shaking in their shoes.

"A fine thing it is that a man cannot be left to lie in his grave in peace," said the ghost of Grandsire MacNab.

"We've been lugging that stone up the road full a week," said the ghost of Grandsire MacRae. "All along o' that old gander of a Sandy MacBean. I'm telling you now, Jamie; Rab was right and you were wrong. The stone is where it ought to be, so leave it there!"

"After Rab quit shifting it we had to do it ourselves." said Jamie's father's ghost.

"And we'll have you know we're not meaning to do so any more. So leave it be, Jamie." commanded the ghost of Rab's father angrily. "'Twas the stream that shifted in the big storm, and not the stone at all."

And two by two and arm in arm the four ghosts turned away and started back to the churchyard.

Halfway down the hill Grandsire MacNab called back to them, "You pass the word to old Sandy MacBean that thinks his memory's so wonderful. Just tell him he'll be with us soon, and when he is, the four of us'll put a flea in his ear about forgetting about that big storm."

So that was the end of the trouble.

Jamie said he had been a dolt to ever listen to old Sandy MacBean in the first place. And Rab said why wouldn't Jamie listen, with old Sandy having such a name for his wonderful memory?

The two lads shook hands with each other over the stone, and after that they were better friends than ever.

Sandy MacBean was the one who suffered most, the poor old bodach! Whenever he said anything about the prodigious memory that he had, someone was sure to ask him how it came about that he forgot the big storm that shifted the burn away from the Boundary stone.

6 / THE LADY'S LOAF-FIELD

THERE ONCE WAS AN OLD LAIRD WHO LOVED ONLY TWO things in the world. They were his wife and his money, and it would have been hard to decide which of the two of them came first with him. He loved his wife enough to give her anything she asked him for—always hoping it wouldn't cost him too much. And he loved his money so much that the only one who could get any of it away from him at all was his wife.

She, poor lady, never asked for much for herself, but she had a great pity for the troubles and sorrows of the poor folks round about. She would ask for them, and although the laird would never give her as much as she asked him for, he always gave her something, which helped somewhat.

Well, the good lady, who had never been strong, fell into an illness, and although the laird and everyone else thought she'd soon be well again, she knew better. So she began to fret to herself about her poor folks and wonder what in the world they'd do when she wasn't there to look after them.

At last she asked the laird to set aside a field to grow grain in, to make loaves for the poor, which they might have for the asking. Well, at first the laird wouldn't hear to it at all. But when she told him it was likely to be the last thing she'd ever be asking him in this life, he grew a little bit frightened. He didn't believe her at all, but to set her mind at ease, he told her that she might have any field of his that she could walk around. He thought she'd have to wait until she was well again to do the walking and by that time maybe she'd have forgotten all about it.

But the lady was too clever for him entirely. The next day she called to her two strong lasses that worked in the castle, and had them take her into the fields. There, she picked out one of the best of the laird's grain fields and then she laid her arms across the lasses' shoulders and, with them supporting her on either side, she walked all the way around the field.

69

When she went back and told the laird what she'd done, he was put out about it, but he had to admit the field was hers, for she'd walked around it and the two lasses could prove it.

The lady was right about its being the last thing she'd ask of him. Not long afterward she died. When she was dying, she told him not to be forgetting about the field he'd given her for her poor folks, and never to be taking it back for himself; because if he did, she'd be sure to know about it.

Well, the old laird set the field aside as he had promised, and he had it plowed and harrowed and seeded year by year. And, year by year, the grain grew better on that field than it did on any of the others. He had the grain reaped and threshed and winnowed and ground, and it was all kept to make loaves for the poor folks. So none of the poor folks round about ever went hungry, because when they wanted a loaf of bread all they needed to do was to ask at the castle for one of the lady's loaves.

The years went by, and now that his lady was gone, the laird had nothing to love but his money, so he began to love that twice as much as he'd ever done before. And he began to cast his eye on the lady's loaf-field, and figure out so many loaves at so many pennies a loaf for so many years past and to come. The amount of money he was losing through that foolish promise was beyond bearing. To make his conscience easy, he told himself that she hadn't really walked around the field herself at all, for she'd had the help of a strapping young lass on either side of her. So he wouldn't be breaking a promise if he took the field for himself after all.

When plowing time came next year, he made up his mind that this time the grain that was grown was going to make money for his pocket and not loaves for the poor.

The word soon got around that there'd be no more loaves at the castle, after the present supply was gone. When the poor folks heard that they couldn't believe their ears. The sound of their grief rose on the air and grew until it reached heaven.

But the laird was set on having his way. The field was plowed and harrowed and seeded, and the grain grew and was reaped and taken to the barn to be threshed and winnowed. But it was not kept to itself to be threshed and gathered into sacks to be ground for the poor folks' loaves. Instead, the laird gave orders that the whole of it was to be thrown in with his own, for he was going to sell it all, and there was to be no more foolishness about the lady's loaf-field.

The next day after that was the one set for the threshing. The men who were to do it were up before daybreak, because there was such a grand heap of grain to be threshed and it being harvest time there was no time to spare. Three or four of them, that were ready first, went to the barn to get the threshing floor and the flails ready for the rest of the men who'd soon be coming along.

They went into the barn laughing and talking, for harvest time is a merry time, what with the jokes and games and feasting that come at the end. But they came out shrieking, and faster than they went in. They rushed along to the castle and met the laird coming out of it on his way up to the barn. They all tried to tell him at the same time, but what with the fright they had on them and the way their teeth chattered and losing their breath running so fast, all that he could make out of what they were trying to say was that there was a ghost and it was in the barn.

"A ghost," said the laird with disgust. "You're a pack o' fools! More like 'tis naught but the old white mare."

So he stomped off up to the barn and in he went.

And there *was* a ghost there. It sat upon the top of one of the heaps of grain, and it was the ghost of his own dead lady.

When she saw him she rose up and she pointed a ghostly finger at him. "I walked the field on my own two feet," said she, "and you gave it me for my own. If you do not thresh my grain for my poor folks' loaves, there'll never be grain threshed in this barn again, for I'll sit here till the end of time ere I e'er let a flail touch a sheaf on this barn's floor."

Well, the laird knew when he was beaten. So he promised the good lady's ghost that he'd never think of breaking his promise again. When she was sure he meant it, she up and disappeared.

The laird had a very difficult time getting the men to come back, but at last he did. The laird had had such a bad fright, he wanted to make sure that there'd be no further trouble. Since he had no way now to tell which were his lady's sheaves and which were his own, having had them all dumped together the way they were, he told the men to thresh all the grain and put it into sacks to be ground. And all of the grain grown on the castle fields that year was made into loaves for the poor folks roundabout. That was a wonderful year for the poor folks, because when one of them was hungry and went to the castle to ask for a loaf of bread, he was given not one but two. And the sound of the poor folks rejoicing grew and increased until it reached heaven. The laird's lady heard it there and was content. She knew the old laird had learned his lesson.

Indeed he had, for he left it in his will that his heirs should always keep that field for the poor. It is so kept until this very day. If you should ever be traveling in those parts you can go up to the castle, and if you just step in and ask they'll take you out and show you the lady's loaf-field.

THERE IS AN OLD TALE TOLD IN SCOTLAND OF HOW THE holy Saint Fillan set himself to copy all the Holy Scriptures from beginning to end. It was a mighty task and a slow one. As he had all his regular work to do besides, he often sat writing long into the night. And they do say that the left hand of Saint Fillan gave off bright light, so that he could see to write in the darkness of the night.

When Saint Fillan died, they took his hand that had the light to it and put it into a silver case and preserved it as a holy relic. It was handed down from one to another for

76

hundreds and hundreds of years, and at last it came to King Robert Bruce of Scotland, who set great store by it.

Well, there was a war going on in Scotland between King Robert Bruce and King Edward of England. Some of the battles had gone against the Scots, and some of them against the English, and they had come to the point of fighting one last big one to decide which side had won the war.

King Robert Bruce was a man of great courage, but he couldn't keep himself from worrying about this battle. So when he left his castle to join his army, he sent for the chaplain who was going with him.

"We'll be needing all the help we can get," he told the chaplain. "So take heed to fetch along with you the silver case with the holy Saint Fillan's hand in it. Having it with us may be a help to us, if the fight goes against us."

The chaplain went to get the relic from the chapel. But when he took the silver case out of the wooden kist where it was kept and held it in his hands, it came into his mind that, if the English should press the Scots hard the holy relic might be lost in the heat of battle. Or, what would be worse, it might fall into the hands of the enemy.

With this thought in his mind, the chaplain took the holy hand out of the case and, wrapping it in a fair white linen cloth, he hid it in a secret closet in the wall of the chapel. Then he locked up the silver case and took it empty to the place where the Scottish army lay.

On the eve of the day when the battle was to be fought, King Robert had with him in his tent his great friend, Angus of the Isles, and his chaplain. The King sat pondering about the morrow and the outcome of the battle and what was going to happen to his army. His mind was sore and anxious, for he had seen the lines of the English army. He knew, from what he had seen, that for every man he had to fight for him, the English king had two or maybe three.

He said to himself that all his hope lay in what help he would get from heaven, so he prepared to spend the night praying to God and Saint Fillan to aid him in the battle.

He told the chaplain to bring the silver case and lay it on the altar that had been set up in the tent. As the chaplain laid the silver case on the altar, he trembled for fear his master might tell him to unlock the casket and throw open the lid. His relief was great, for the king did not ask him to do so. So the case, locked and empty, lay there upon the altar, and the chaplain's theft was not discovered.

The three of them—King Robert Bruce, Angus of the Isles, and the chaplain—knelt praying side by side. Suddenly the lid of the silver case flew up, and a light shone through the tent from it. Then the case snapped shut again.

King Robert and Angus saw naught but the light, as they looked up from their prayers, bewildered and amazed. But the guilty chaplain saw a monk in a coarse brown habit standing with one hand on the lid of the case. The monk

looked at him sternly, and the chaplain put his hands up before his face to shut out the awful sight. When he took his hands down to look again, the monk had disappeared.

The chaplain rushed to the altar, and finding the case unlocked, he threw back the lid. Lying in the case was Saint Fillan's hand, still wrapped in the white linen cloth as the chaplain had wrapped it when he hid it away in the chapel of the castle! Then it was that the chaplain knew that the monk was the apparition of Saint Fillan himself, who had brought his hand back to the silver case.

The chaplain cried out, "A miracle! A miracle!" and he cast himself at the feet of King Robert Bruce and confessed what he had done. The King was merciful and raised the chaplain gently from the ground, telling him that where his fault lay was in not having faith that Saint Fillan would be able to protect his own hand.

They took it for a sign from heaven and spent all the rest of the night till morn had come again in prayer and praise.

Then they went out to battle, and though they were greatly outnumbered by the English, King Robert Bruce and his Scots were victorious and won the war at the Battle of Bannockburn.

8 / THE MAN O' THE CLAN

THERE WAS ONE OF THE MacDONALDS ONCE WHO HAD gotten a bit discontented over the way things were going after the clans were out to fight for Bonnie Prince Charlie and had been put down again by the English. This Ian MacDonald took it into his head to take to his heels and save himself from further trouble. So overseas to America he went, with a number of other lads who thought they'd rather keep their heads on their shoulders than have them cut off.

When he left, he had the intention of coming back again as soon as the troubled times were forgotten, but what with being busy making his fortune and one thing or another, he never did.

By the time old Ian MacDonald died, there were four more generations of MacDonalds in the new country where he'd settled. Not one of them had ever laid eyes on Scotland, though all of them said they were going there, just as old Ian had said. There was always something that came along to stop them, like the dangers and discomforts of ocean travel in those days, and the American Wars coming on as they did—and, besides, they were all busy making their fortunes, too. But every single one of them was as crammed full as a Michaelmas goose with old tales that had been handed down to them from one generation to another, and there wasn't one of the lot that wouldn't have taken his oath that you could set him down blindfolded anywhere in the Highlands and he'd be able to find his way with no trouble at all.

It wasn't until the grandson five times removed from old Ian came along that any of the family got back to the old country. The others had been talking about it for nearly one hundred-fifty years, but this grandson made up his mind he'd go and see for himself when he got to be a man. He was as full of the old tales that had come down in the family as all the rest, but he was a sensible chap, so he told himself he'd not be disappointed if things didn't come up to his expecta-

tions, because all he had to go by were the old tales, which, he had to admit, were more than second-hand by the time he got them.

He made the journey with no mishap, since ships had greatly improved since old Ian's day, and one fine morning, after a lot of traveling o'er sea and land, he set his foot on the soil of his forefathers' land.

Strange to say, he had no reason to be disappointed, because everything was just about the way they'd told him 'twould be. The mountains and lochs and glens were beyond compare, and he had the good luck to meet up with some of the MacDonalds whose ancestors had stayed behind when old Ian and his lot had left Scotland. They took a fancy to him, maybe because he admired everything so much and didn't mind saying so. Anyway, he was a member of the American branch of the clan and in the family, so to speak. So he had a grand time being passed along from one to another and never a chance to be lonely. Before his visit was half over, he'd begun to wish he could stay twice as long as he'd planned.

He'd left off going to see Culloden Field until the last. That was the most important place to him, for it was from Culloden Field that his great-great-great-great grandfather, old Ian MacDonald, had fled during the troubled times. Usually, he had company for his sightseeing trips, but there were no available MacDonalds about the day he went there, so he had to go by himself.

He jogged along at a pleasant pace, because the weather   83 was fine and he wanted a look at the countryside as he went by.

He came into Culloden shortly before noon. When he asked at a hotel how much farther he had to go, they told him 'twas a matter of maybe four miles or so, and he'd not be o'erlong getting there.

He thought they looked at him a bit oddly when he asked, but they answered him civilly enough so he put the thought out of his mind. He decided he'd have his meal before he started out, and then he'd not have to think about hurrying back for his dinner. He sent his horse around to the stables to be tended and went on into the dining room of the hotel.

Being early, he had the place to himself, and the man who waited on the table being a friendly-looking old fellow, young MacDonald talked to him while he ate. They talked about the weather being fine for the middle of April and about the places of interest in the neighborhood and then MacDonald mentioned that he was on his way to Culloden Field.

The waiter stopped in his work. He looked MacDonald square in the face for a moment. Then he asked slowly, "Happen some of your own folks was there, sir?"

"I'm a MacDonald," the other answered. "My folks were there."

"Och aye," the waiter said, "MacDonalds was there. Some o' them stayed there." He seemed to be about to say more, but as he didn't, young MacDonald went on with his meal, and presently the waiter went away. He came back just as MacDonald finished, and said, "You were speaking of going to the Field, sir. Happen ye'd be preferring to see the old forts and suchlike here today, and stay over to see the Field on the morrow? There'd be a guide could take you then, but they're all off today."

"Oh, I can't do that," said MacDonald. "My plans are made, and I must start back as soon as I've seen Culloden. I'd not have the time to take another day."

"'Tis not the best day for it," the waiter said, shaking his head. "The morrow would be better."

MacDonald could not understand what he meant by that, for he'd never seen a day so fair and clear. But people were beginning to come into the room, so he paid his bill and sent for his horse and soon was on his way.

He asked for directions as he left, and they told him just to keep on the high road till he'd gone about four miles. He'd come to a wood and the Field would be just by it.

He came to the high road they had told him to take, turned into it, and rode on easily, trying to remember the tales the folks at home had told him.

He didn't know just when the queer feeling began, but it must have been when he'd gone about a mile on his way. He seemed to be riding on a road he'd ridden before, through country he knew well—which was plain impossible for it was

85

his first time in Scotland and he'd never been anywhere near this part of the place.

He was turning that over in his mind and he didn't notice where the man came from, but all of a sudden he was there, going along beside young MacDonald's horse with one hand holding to the saddle. The horse had quickened its pace, but the man ran easily beside it.

When MacDonald looked down at him, the man lifted his free hand in greeting. "Speed a bit, Ian MacDonald" said the man, "or ye'll be late forebye!"

"Who are you?" MacDonald asked.

"I'm a man o' the clan," the man answered.

"What will we be late for?" asked MacDonald then.

The man made no answer. The horse was running faster, but the man kept pace with it, still with his hand on the saddle. MacDonald remembered that he had been told that so the unmounted men ran beside their lairds when going into battle. He looked the fellow over and saw that he was wearing Highland dress; his kilt and hose were patterned in the MacDonald tartan and he wore the short double-edged sword hanging from his belt. All dressed up in costume, MacDonald thought to himself. They must have found a guide at the hotel after all and sent him out after me. It was nice of them.

By this time the horse's pace had become too fast to please him. He tried to rein it in, but the horse paid him no

heed. The next thing he noticed was that somehow they must have missed the road, for the horse was galloping over a rolling moor with neither road nor path to break it, and though they had surely come four miles there was no wood in sight at all.

Then, all of a sudden, he heard the skirl of bagpipes and the answering scream of the pipes from the other side of the moor. There, before him, to his amazement, were two armies drawn up facing each other. He pulled as hard as he could on the reins, rising in his stirrups to do so, but the horse swept on. Just at that moment a cannon roared. The two lines of men rushed at each other; swords flashed in the sunlight; there was the sound of musket fire; and all about him was tumult and noise and confusion.

The horse leaped forward, and there MacDonald was in the thick of it, with the man o' the clan still beside him. The man was wielding the sword with unusual skill, protecting MacDonald, who was at a disadvantage having no weapon at all. Suddenly, the man o' the clan caught at his breast, and the red blood ran down through his fingers. "I can do no more!" he cried, and, falling, he pressed his sword into Mac-Donald's hand.

MacDonald clutched the sword, but before he could use it, a tall soldier ran at him with a raised musket and fired at him. MacDonald felt a sharp pain in his shoulder, and then he fell to the ground and saw no more of the battle.

88

When he came to his senses, he found himself back in the hotel with a doctor hanging over him. He tried to get up, but the doctor held him back. "Come now!" said the doctor. "Be a good lad and lie easy!"

"I was shot!" MacDonald said.

"Och nay!" said the doctor. "You were not shot at all. You fell from your horse and broke your shoulder."

"But the battle . . ." MacDonald cried.

"Whisht, lad," said the doctor, "there was no shot. You fell from your horse onto the road and your shoulder got broke in the fall."

"There was a battle," MacDonald insisted.

"Och nay. There was no battle the day," the doctor said. "Your horse came running back to the town with the saddle empty, and folks went out and found you there in the road where he'd thrown you."

MacDonald was not to be convinced. They may have picked him up and brought him back to the town, but there was no road and there *was* a battle. He had been in the very middle of it, and it must be going on yet.

The doctor only smiled and shook his head. "Nay, I'm telling you true, There is no battle this day. But there was one a hundred and fifty years ago. That is the one you saw."

So that's the way it was. The day young Ian MacDonald had chosen to visit Culloden Field was the sixteenth of April, and without planning it at all, he'd managed to get there just

89

an hour after noontide. And it was on the sixteenth of April, 1746, at that same hour that the battle had begun. What MacDonald had seen was two armies of ghosts fighting the battle all over again!

He stayed at the hotel a while till his shoulder healed itself, and while he was there, the old waiter told him that those who had folks in the battle those long years ago had often been known to see it. Providing, of course, they got there on the right day and at the right hour.

It was a strange thing, however, that it was from Culloden Field old Ian MacDonald had fled overseas to save his life. And back over the seas, a hundred and fifty years later, his great-great-great-great grandson had come to take part in the ghostly battle of Culloden Field.

IF YOU SHOULD EVER BE TRAVELING THROUGH THE TROSSACHS beyond the town of Callander, you'll happen to come to a bit of a village. There's not really much to the village, barring a post office and a tavern, a shop or two, and the kirk. It's the kirk you'll want to be noticing, or rather the kirkyard beside it. In the kirkyard there's a gravestone that has a very strange story to it. More like a monument it is than a gravestone, for it is in the shape of a couch and upon it lies the stone figure of a fine old man. There's a huge stone dog crouched on either side of the couch, so big that the dogs' heads are well above the level of it. The man's hands lie on the heads of the stone dogs, and on his face is the sort of a smile that makes it seem as if something had given him great satisfaction.

The man was the laird of the manor just beyond the village, and a very good man he was and greatly loved by all his tenants. Maybe he wasn't exactly a saint, but even now, long after, you'd have a hard time making the folks who live on his estates believe he wasn't. He could be a hard man when he wanted to, and he could fly into a terrible rage if he was stirred to do so, but somebody'd have to do something terribly bad before he'd let his anger loose on them.

He had but one son, and that one as fine a man as his father in every way. The son was an officer in the king's army, and the old laird was terribly proud of him, as he well might be.

There's always at least one black sheep in every family, and in the laird's family it was his nephew. He was a carousing good-for-nothing fellow, and nothing the laird could do or say would make him change. The laird put up with him as long as he could, but at last his evil ways were past bearing any longer, so the laird turned him off for good.

The laird had two dogs that he had raised from the time that they were old enough to be taken from their mother. Being a lonely man, with his wife long dead and his soldier son having to be away so often, he brought the two dogs into the house and trained them to be house dogs to keep him company. He grew fond of the dogs, and they of him, and even when they were wee whelps they were always at his side. You'd have thought for sure that he had them on some sort of leash, they kept so close beside him always; but all that bound them to him was their love.

Whether he was at table or walking about his estates or resting in his manor, there they were too. And at night they lay on the floor on either side of his bed to keep watch over him while he slept. From the day he got them, and they so small that they tumbled all over their own feet, nobody ever saw the laird without his two dogs.

By the time they were a year old they'd got their growth and they were the talk of the country for miles around because of their monstrous size. Nobody had ever seen the like of them before, and strangers used to stop in their tracks to stare at the dogs, not believing their eyes.

One day the laird's son came home with his babe in his arms. The child's mother had died, and the laird's son had been ordered off to the foreign wars. He could neither take the wee lad with him nor stay behind himself to care for him, so he brought him to the old laird to keep for him until he could come back home.

The laddie thrived and grew, and soon was the dearie and the darling of the laird and all the folks in the manor and on the estates. Not that anyone spoiled him, for they knew the old laird would not have liked that. But everybody took a hand in bringing him up and were pleased to do it. Even the laird's dogs were fond of him, although they'd never let him coax them away from the old laird's side. There was only one time they ever left their places there, and that was after the old laird was dead.

When the laddie was six years old or thereabouts, they had the word that the laird's son had been killed in one of those foreign battles. News was scarce in those days and often traveled slow and in a roundabout way, sometimes being the truth and sometimes not. The laird said he didn't believe it, and wouldn't until he had more proof than a bit of wandering gossip. But after that, he began to think a lot about his grandson's future. He was growing to be an old man, and he wasn't as strong as he'd have liked to be. It bothered him to think of what could happen should he die and the young lad be left alone in the world with no one to watch over him. It might have been a premonition that he had. However that may be, before another year had passed, the old laird caught some sort of fever and, in spite of all the doctors could do, he died.

The two dogs laid themselves down in their places by his bed. They gave one long mournful howl of grief and laid their heads down on their paws. When folks came to carry the old laird down to the kirkyard, they found the dogs lying there dead as the old laird himself.

Everybody said that having lived all their days in this

world with the laird, they had followed him out of it now to be with him in the next. So they took them, too, and buried them with the laird, because they thought he'd want it to be that way.

The stonecutter made the old laird's tomb with the old laird lying on his couch and a dog lying at either side of it, just as they were at the end. Only, when he carved it, the dogs' heads were down on their paws and the old laird's arms were crossed on his breast. And he wasn't smiling at all.

So now the wee bit of a lad was laird of the manor and heir to all the money and the estates, unless his father was not dead and came home to take them over.

When the wicked nephew heard that the old laird was dead, he wasn't unhappy about it at all. The news that the laird's son had been killed in battle had come to his ears too, and he was only too ready to believe it. He told himself that all he had to do was to get rid of the laddie, and then he'd be the next heir to the estates and he'd be laird of the manor and all that went with it.

He made up his mind to steal the wee lad out of his bed while he was sleeping. He'd carry the child to the seacoast to a sea captain he knew who would be willing to take the lad to foreign parts and leave him there. The nephew didn't care where it was, as long as it was too far for the lad to find his way back home again.

So he sought out a friend as bad as himself to go with

him. They chose a wild dark stormy night, so that few people would be abroad to see them. When they got to the manor, they found it dark and all within it sound asleep. They got in very quietly, so as not to arouse the people in the house, and the wicked nephew sent his friend upstairs to fetch the lad while he himself looked about to find some money with which to pay the sea captain for his trouble.

He never heard his friend go up the stairs, because he crept up so quietly. But he heard him coming down! The fellow was half-tumbling, half-racing down the steps, taking them three or four at a time.

The nephew picked up his candle and ran out into the hall.

"Be quiet, you fool!" he whispered. "Will you have the whole house awake and after us?"

Then he saw his friend's face. It had such a look of fear as he'd never seen before. It was as white as the tallow candle itself and with wild rolling eyes.

"What ails you?" the nephew asked sharply.

All the answer he got was, "I saw . . . I saw . . . I saw . . ." But what his friend saw, he never said. With shaking hands, the friend unbolted the door and ran out into the dark of the night outside.

"Well, if he'll not tell me what's amiss, I'll go and look for myself," said the laird's nephew. And up the stairs he went.

The door of the lad's room was open and a light shone out. The laird's nephew went down the hall to the door. Then he stopped and stared. There was a night light on the table by the bed, and in the bed the lad lay sleeping sweetly. But it wasn't at the lad the nephew was looking.

At the foot of the bed stood the old laird that he knew had been in his grave for many a long day. And at either side of the old laird stood one of the great dogs that had been buried with him.

While the nephew stood as if frozen on the doorsill staring at them, the old laird slowly lifted his hand and pointed a finger at him. And as if it were a signal, the two dogs, who in life and in death had never before left their master's side, leaped forward.

With a shriek of terror the old laird's nephew turned and fled down the stairs. The giant dogs pursued him out of the house and down the road. Faster and faster and faster they went, and above the sound of the storm outside, their baying filled the night.

It was that same night that the old laird's son came home. He'd not been killed in the wars at all. 'Twas what the old laird had said.

They told the son in the village that his father was long dead. He set out for the manor feeling very sad and mournful. As he was climbing the hill, he heard a sound that made him stop to listen.

"'Tis a very strange thing!" he told himself. "If they had not said in the village that my father's dogs lay in his grave with him, I'd swear that was them baying after some quarry down the glen."

Well, that's all to the story. The nephew's friend was found lying in the fields next day and babbled out the part of it he knew, and folks pieced the rest of it together. The nephew was never seen nor heard of again, but they do say that on a wild dark stormy night you can hear the laird's dogs baying down the glen, and folks will tell you that they are still hunting down the old laird's wicked nephew.

Maybe the strangest part of all was what came after. When folks came to the kirk on Sunday for the services, they stopped amazed in the kirkyard. The figure of the old laird lay no longer with its arms crossed on its breast. Nor were the dogs' heads down on their paws as the stonecutter had carved them. They saw that the dogs now crouched by the bed with their stone heads erect and alert. And upon the head of the dog on either side lay one of the old laird's hands. And upon the face of the old laird lay a happy, satisfied smile.

THERE ONCE WAS A HOUSE THAT LACKED A BOGLE. THAT would be no great thing for a house to be wanting in the ordinary way, but it happened that this house was in St. Andrews. That being a town where every one of the best houses has a ghost or a bogle, as they call it, of its own, or maybe two or even more, the folks who lived in the house felt the lack sorely. They were terribly ashamed when their friends talked about their bogles, seeing that they had none of their own.

100

The worst of it was that they had but lately come into money and had bought the house to set themselves up in the world. They never thought to ask if it had a bogle when they bought it, just taking it for granted that it had. But what good was it to be having a fine big house if there was no bogle in it? In St. Andrews, anyway!

The man of the house could be reckoned a warm man with a tidy lot of money at his banker's, while his neighbor MacParlan had a hard time of it scraping enough to barely get by. But the MacParlan's had a bogle that had been in the family since the time of King Kenneth the First, and they had papers to prove it.

The woman of the house had two horses to her carriage, and Mrs. MacNair had no carriage at all. But the MacNairs had *three* bogles, being well supplied, and Mrs. MacNair was so set up about them that it fair put one's teeth on edge to hear her going on about them and their doings.

Tammas, the son of the house, told his parents that he couldn't hold up his head when chaps talked about their bogles at his school, and he had to admit that there weren't any at his house at all.

And then there was Jeannette, the daughter of the house (her name was really Janet but she didn't like the sound of it, it being so plain). Well, *she* came home one day, and banged the door to, and burst into tears. And when they all asked her what was amiss, she said she'd been humiliated entirely

because they hadn't a bogle, and she'd never show her face outside the house again until her papa got one for her.

Well, it all came to this. Without a bogle, they could cut no figure at all in society, for all their money.

They did what they could, of course, to set the matter right. In fact, each one of them tried in his own way, but not letting on to the others, however, lest they be disappointed if naught came of it.

The man of the house kept an eye on MacParlan's house and found out that MacParlan's bogle liked to take a stroll by nights on the leads of MacParlan's roof. So one night, when all the MacParlans had gone off somewhere away from home, he went over and called up to MacParlan's bogle. After a bit of havering, the man got down to the point. "Do you not get terrible tired of haunting the same old place day in and and day out?" he asked.

"What way would I be doing that?" the bogle asked, very much surprised.

"Och, 'twas just a thought I had," said the man. "You might be liking to visit elsewhere maybe?"

"That I would not," said the bogle flatly.

"Och well," said the man, "should you e'er feel the need o' a change of scene, you'll find a warm welcome at my house any time and for as long as you're liking to stay."

The bogle peered down at him over the edge of the roof.

"Thank you kindly," said he, "but I'll bide here wi' my

own folks. So dinna expect me." And with that he disappeared.

So there was naught for the man to do but go back home.

The woman of the house managed to get herself asked to the MacNairs' house for tea. She took with her a note to the MacNairs' bogles, telling them she was sure the three of them must be a bit cramped for room, what with there being so many of them and the MacNairs' house being so small. So she invited any or all of them to come over and stay at her house, where they'd find plenty of room and every comfort provided that a bogle could ever wish.

When nobody was watching, she slipped the note down behind the wainscoting in the MacNairs' drawing room, where she was sure the MacNairs' bogles would be finding it.

The MacNairs' bogles found it all right, and it surprised them. They didn't know exactly what to make of the note when they'd read it. But there was no doubt the woman meant it kindly, they said to each other. Being very polite bogles, they decided that she deserved the courtesy of an answer to the note, and since none of them was very much for writing, the least they could do was to send one of themselves to decline the invitation. The woman had paid them a call, so to speak. So one of them went to attend to it that same night.

The bogle met up with the woman of the house just as she was coming out of the linen press with a pile of fresh

towels in her arms. The maids had left that day, being un-
willing to remain in a house so inferior that it had no bogle
to it. She'd have been startled out of her wits had she not
been so glad to see the bogle.

"Och then!" said she, "'tis welcome you are entirely!"

"Thank ye kindly," said the bogle.

"You'll be stopping here I hope?" questioned the
woman eagerly.

"I'm sorry to be disappointing you," said the bogle,
"but I'm not staying. I'm needed at home."

"Och now," said the woman, "and could they not make
do without you just for a month or two? Or happen even a
fortnight?"

But she could see for herself that the bogle was not to
be persuaded. In fact, none of them could accept her invitation. That's what the bogle had come to tell her. With
their thanks, of course.

"'Tis a sore thing," complained the woman, "what with
all the money paid out for the house and all, that we have no
bogle of our own. Now can you be telling me why?"

"I would not like to say," said the bogle.

But the woman was sure he knew the reason, so she
pressed him until at last the bogle said reluctantly, "Well,
this is the way of it. The house is too young! Losh! 'Tis not
anywhere near a hundred years old yet, and there's not been
time enough for anything to have happened that would bring   105

it a bogle of its own. And forebye . . ." The bogle stopped talking at that point.

"Och! What more?" urged the woman.

"We-e-ell," said the bogle slowly, "I'd not be liking to hurt your feelings, but your family is not, so to speak, distinguished enough. Now you take the MacParlans and the Macphersons and the MacAlistairs—their families go back into the far ages. And the MacAlpines is as old as the hills and rocks and streams. As for the MacNairs," he added proudly, "och, well, the MacNairs *is* the MacNairs. The trouble with your family is that there is nothing of note to it. No one knows exactly where it would be belonging. There's no clan or sept o' the name. Losh! The name has not even a 'Mac' at the front of it."

"Aye," said the woman slowly, "I can see that fine."

And so she could. For the truth was that they had come from Wigtown and were not a Highland family at all.

"Well," said the bogle, "that's the way it is. So I'll bid you good night." And away he went like a drift of mist, leaving the poor woman of the house alone and uncomforted.

The daughter of the house had taken to her bed and spent her time there, weeping and sleeping, when she wasn't eating sweeties out of a pink satin box and reading romantic tales about lovely ladies who had adventures in castles just teeming with ghosts and handsome gentlemen in velvet suits of clothes.

So there was no one left to have a try but the son, Tammas. It must be admitted he did the best he could, even if it turned out that he was maybe a little bit too successful.

Tammas had got to the place where he kept out of the way of his friends on account of the shame that was on the family; he being young and full of pride. He only went out by night, taking long walks in lonely places all by himself.

One night he was coming back from one of these walks, and he came along by a kirkyard. It was just the sort of spot that suited his gloomy thoughts, so he stopped and leaned over the wall to look at the long rows of gravestones.

"All those graves lying there," he thought, "with many a bogle from them stravaging through the town and not a one of them for us. 'Tis not fair on us."

He stopped to think about the injustice of it, and then he said out loud, "If there's a bogle amongst you all who's got no family of his own, let him just come along with me. He can bide with us and welcome." And with a long, deep sigh he turned back up the road and started for home.

He'd not gone more than twenty paces past the end of the kirkyard, when of a sudden he heard a fearful noise behind him. It was so eery that it near raised the hair right off from his head. It sounded like a cat yowling and a pig squealing and a horse neighing and an ox bellowing all at one and the same time.

Tammas scarcely dared turn and look, with the fright

that was on him, but turn he did. And he saw 'twas a man coming toward him. He was dressed in Highland dress with kilt and sporran, jacket and plaid showing plain, and the moonlight glinting off of his brooch and shoe buckles and off the handle of the dirk in his hose. He carried a pair of bagpipes under his arm and that was where the noise was coming from.

"Whisht, man," called Tammas, "leave off with the pipes now. The racket you're making's enough to wake the dead."

"'Twill do no such thing," said the piper. "For they're all awake already and about their business. As they should be, it being midnight."

And he put his mouth at the pipes to give another blow.

"Och, then ye'll wake all the folks in St. Andrews," protested Tammas. "Give over now, that's a good lad!"

"Och nay," said the piper soothingly. "St. Andrew folks will pay us no heed. They're used to us. They even like us."

By this time he had come up to Tammas where he stood in the middle of the road. Tammas took another look at him to see who the piper was. And losh, 'twas no man at all. 'Twas a bogle!

"'Tis a strangely queer thing," said the piper sadly. "I've been blowin' on these dommed things all the days of my mortal life till I plain blew the life out o' my body doing it. And I've been blowing on them two or three hundred years since then, and I just cannot learn how to play a tune on them."

"Well, go blow somewhere else," Tammas told him. "Where it's lonely-like, with none to hear you."

"I'd not be liking that at all," said the piper. "Besides, I'm coming along with you."

"With me!" Tammas cried in alarm.

"Och aye," said the piper, and then he added reproach-fully, "you asked me, you know. Did you not?"

"I suppose I did," Tammas admitted reluctantly. "But I'd no idea there'd be anyone there listening."

"Well *I* was there," the piper said, "and I was listening. I doubt that I'm the only bogle in the place without a family of my own. So I accept the invitation, and thank ye kindly. Let's be on our way."

And off he stepped, with his kilt swinging and his arms squared just so and the pipes going at full blast.

Tammas went along with him, because there was no-where else he could go at that hour but back to his home.

When they got home, Tammas opened the door and into the house the two of them went. All the family came running to see what was up, for the pipes sounded worse in-doors than out since there was less room there for the horrible noise to spread.

"There!" Tammas shouted at them all, raising his voice 109

over the racket of the bagpipes. "There's your bogle for you, and I hope you're all satisfied!"

And he stomped up the stairs and into his room, where he went to bed with his pillow pulled over his ears.

Strange to tell, they really were satisfied, because now they had a bogle and could hold their own when they went out into society. Quite nicely as it happened, for they had the distinction of being the only family in the town that had a piping ghost—even if he didn't know how to play the pipes.

It all turned out very well, after all. The daughter of the house married one of the sons of the MacNairs and changed her name back to Janet, her husband liking it better. And she had a "Mac" at the front of her name at last, as well as her share of the three MacNair bogles, so she was perfectly happy.

The mother and father grew a bit deaf with age, and the piping didn't trouble them at all.

But Tammas decided he'd had all he wanted of bogles and of St. Andrews as well. So he went off to London where he made his fortune and became a real Sassenach. In time, he even got a "Sir" before his name, which gave him a lot more pleasure than he'd ever have got from a "Mac."

The bogle never did learn to play the bagpipes, though he never left off trying. But nobody cared about that at all. Not even the bogle.